Specials!

Diversity and values

Eileen Osborne and Steph Yates

Acknowledgements

© 2008 Folens Limited, on behalf of the author.

United Kingdom: Folens Publishers, Waterslade House, Thame Road, Haddenham, Buckinghamshire, HP17 8NT.
Email: folens@folens.com

Ireland: Folens Publishers, Greenhills Road, Tallaght, Dublin 24.
Email: info@folens.ie

Editor: Kayleigh Buller

Layout artist: Planman Technologies

Cover design: Martin Cross

Cover image: © iStockphoto.com/William Schultz

Illustrations: Bridget Dowty of GCI

First published 2008 by Folens Limited.

British Library Cataloguing in Publication Data. A catalogue record for this publication is available from the British Library.

ISBN 978-1-85008-376-4

Contents

Introduction

Specials! PSHE Diversity and Values helps students appreciate diversity within the UK. It looks at the values shared by people from different communities and gives students the opportunity to think about their own values.

This is one of six books in the Specials PSHE series which can be used together to cover many of the requirements for PSHE at Key Stage 3.

The teacher can work in different ways. Each unit could be taught as one or two lessons with students working individually, in pairs or in groups. Alternatively, a single Resource sheet and related Activity sheet(s) could be used as required. The book is divided into ten units. Each unit has one or more photocopiable Resource sheets and several Activity sheets.

The Teacher's notes give guidance and are laid out as follows:

Objectives
These are the main skills or knowledge to be learned.

Prior knowledge
This refers to the minimum skills or knowledge required by students to complete the tasks. As a rule, students should have a reading and comprehension age of six to ten years. Some Activity sheets are more challenging than others and will need to be selected accordingly.

Links
All units link to aspects of the PSHE QCA framework at Key Stage 3, as well as the PSE/PSD guidelines for Scotland, Wales and Northern Ireland.

Background
This gives additional information including facts and figures for the teacher about particular aspects of the topic.

Starter activity
Since the units can be taught as a lesson, a warm-up activity focusing on an aspect of the unit is suggested.

Resource sheets and Activity sheets
The Resource sheets contain no tasks or activities and can be used as a stimulus for discussion. Where useful, keywords are given in the Teacher's notes and related tasks are provided on the Activity sheets. Links with other Activity sheets are sometimes indicated.

Plenary
The teacher can use the suggestions here to do additional work, recap on the main points covered, or reinforce a particular point.

Assessment sheet
At the end of the book there is an Assessment sheet focusing on student progress and learning. It can be used in different ways. A student could complete it as a self-assessment, while the teacher or support assistant also completes one on the student's progress. The two can then be compared and contrasted during a discussion. Alternatively, students could work in pairs and carry out peer-assessments and then compare outcomes.

The use of 'faces', rather than comments, allow students to complete the sheet quickly and easily once the meaning of the three facial expressions have been explained to them. The sheet also allows students to set targets for the next series of lessons.

Look out for other titles in the PSHE series, including:
- Careers and economic understanding
- Drugs
- Healthy lifestyles
- Personal Finance
- Relationships

Teacher's notes

What do we mean by diversity?

Objectives

- To understand that diversity is an essential part of the human race
- To consider the advantages of diversity
- To look at ways of accommodating different beliefs
- To think about ways of celebrating diversity

Prior knowledge

Students require no prior knowledge for this unit.

Links to the PSHE: Personal Well-being KS3 Programme of Study for England

1.1 Personal identities
1.5 Diversity

Links to the Draft Curriculum for Excellence for Scotland

Health and Well-being: Relationships
Social Studies: People, past events and societies

Links to the Personal and Social Education Framework for Wales

Community aspect
Social aspect

Links to the Learning for Life and Work: Local and Global Citizenship requirements for Northern Ireland

Diversity and inclusion

Background

Diversity can be a source of richness, providing a range of skills and abilities and creating a vibrant and positive community. It can also be a cause of conflict, creating division and unhappiness. Unfortunately, the media tend to focus on the more negative aspects of diversity. Discussions about diversity are often narrowed down to ethnic and religious diversity, but it can be thought of in much wider terms to encompass people with different abilities, opinions, attitudes, aspirations, values and ways of life. For students, the easiest way of answering the question, 'what do we mean by diversity?' is probably in the single word, 'differences'.

Starter activity

Pose the question, 'Are people more alike than they are different, or more different than they are alike?'. Have a brief discussion and then let students vote on the answer.

Resource sheets and Activity sheets

Students can read the cartoon on the Resource sheet, 'The last 50 humans', before completing the Activity sheet, 'Saving the human race', in small groups. The groups should then share their decisions as a class.

The Activity sheet, 'Diversity gets things done', reinforces the fact that society relies on people having different abilities, skills and preferences.

The Activity sheet, 'Different beliefs', begins to look at the diversity of beliefs and how this can sometimes cause problems. Students should be encouraged to think of solutions which will enable the people to keep their beliefs, even if the students do not agree with the beliefs themselves. You could talk about compromise and how this is not always a solution to matters of belief. For example, it is not good to ask a committed vegetarian to eat meat occasionally. A more able group could also think about what happens when one group's beliefs are directly opposed to another's, for example, should a racist person be free to act on their beliefs?

The Activity sheet, 'Celebrating diversity', could be completed in pairs, with each partner designing one side of the leaflet. You might be able to tie this in with events in your local area.

Plenary

Ask each of the students to think of one way in which they are different from everyone else in the class. Get them to write it out on a piece of paper in decorative writing and stick them all together to make a class diversity poster. You could give some examples to begin with to encourage a range of interesting ideas, for example, 'I am the only one who plays the clarinet', or 'I am the only one who lives in a caravan'.

The last 50 humans

Planet Earth is about to be destroyed by a huge meteorite…

This spaceship is our only hope of saving the human race. It can take 50 people.

Yes. With luck they will find a new planet. The rest of the human race will be destroyed by the meteorite.

We should choose 50 people of all ages and races, rich and poor, strong and weak, with a wide range of different interests and abilities. They must represent the whole of humankind.

No! Differences are what cause problems and war on Earth. We have a chance to create a peaceful human society for the first time ever. We must choose 50 people who are as alike as possible. They should want the same things and have the same skills. They should be equally clever, and have the same opinions on things. In this way, we will create a glorious human society where everyone is happy and there is no fighting.

Activity sheet – What do we mean by diversity?

Saving the human race

Read the story on the Resource sheet, 'The last 50 humans'. Imagine you are part of the group of people trying to decide who to send in the spaceship.

☞ 1 Fill in the chart below to help you decide which plan to follow.

	Advantages	Disadvantages
Plan A: Send 50 very different people to represent the whole of the human race.		
Plan B: Send 50 very similar people to try to create a new, peaceful human race.		

☞ 2 Discuss the advantages and disadvantages of each plan. Now decide which plan you think the group should choose. Record your ideas below.

I think we should choose plan _____ because _____

_____

_____

Diversity gets things done

The people below all work for the RSPCA. They all have one thing in common, they care about animals. But they have many differences. Their differences are what make them good at their jobs.

☞ 1 Read their comments and the job descriptions, then fill in the gaps to show which job you think each person does.

"I am very enthusiastic and enjoy working with people."

My job is _____

"I didn't do well at school but I'm good at physical work and I am quite happy working on my own or with other people."

My job is _____

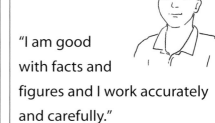

"I am good with facts and figures and I work accurately and carefully."

My job is _____

"I have good writing skills and am very organised."

My job is _____

"People say I am very clever. I can cope with a lot of pressure and can think problems through."

My job is _____

"I am very patient and can stay calm in difficult situations. I am good with people."

My job is _____

Fund-raiser – Working with groups to help them set up fun fund-raising events.

Office worker – Taking care of all the paperwork.

Vet – Taking care of the animals when they are ill.

Centre worker – Cleaning out, feeding and exercising the animals.

Accountant – Taking care of the money and finances.

Welfare officer – Visiting places where animals are being badly treated and giving advice or taking animals away.

☞ 2 Diversity means differences. What would happen to an organisation like the RSPCA if there was no diversity and everyone had the same skills, abilities and interests?

Diversity and values

Activity sheet – What do we mean by diversity?

Different beliefs

One way in which people show their diversity is through the things they believe. Sometimes different beliefs can cause problems, but there is usually a solution.

☞ 1 Write down possible solutions to the problems below which will allow these people to keep to their beliefs. Write your solutions on a separate piece of paper.

"I don't believe that it's right to have sex before marriage. I've had boyfriends in the past that dumped me because I wouldn't sleep with them. Now I'm cautious of going out with anyone."

"I am Jewish and at home we abide by the rules of kosher very strictly. I travel a lot for work and in some places it is impossible to find hotels which will serve kosher food."

"Since my wife died I have been going to a spiritualist who has contacted my wife. My children think I am being taken advantage of and wasting my money. They want me to stop going."

It is easy to keep to your beliefs if everyone around you shares the same ideas. It can be difficult if few people share your beliefs and even more difficult if other people think that your beliefs are wrong or stupid.

☞ 2 Design a poster encouraging everyone to respect other people's beliefs. Try to include reasons for why this is important.

Activity sheet – What do we mean by diversity?

Celebrating diversity

You are part of a committee which is planning to put on a festival celebrating diversity in you local area.

☞ 1 The committee have begun making a list of things which could be part of the festival. Add another six items to the list.

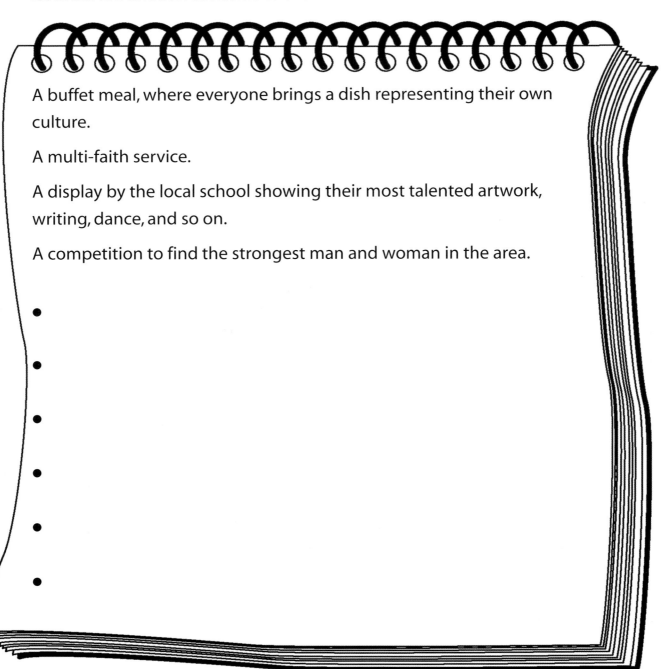

A buffet meal, where everyone brings a dish representing their own culture.

A multi-faith service.

A display by the local school showing their most talented artwork, writing, dance, and so on.

A competition to find the strongest man and woman in the area.

-
-
-
-
-
-

☞ 2 Now design a leaflet advertising your festival of diversity. It should include why you are holding the festival as well as what is going to be on.

Diversity and values

Teacher's notes

A multicultural, multi-faith society

Objectives

- To understand that the UK contains people of different faiths and cultures
- To look at some of the things which make up a person's culture
- To reflect on how people of different cultures and faiths can work together

Prior knowledge

Students will need to know that different religious groups worship in different places.

Links to the PSHE: Personal Well-being KS3 Programme of Study for England

1.1 Personal identities
1.5 Diversity

Links to the Draft Curriculum for Excellence for Scotland

Health and Well-being: Relationships
Social Studies: People, past events and societies

Links to the Personal and Social Education Framework for Wales

Community aspect
Social aspect

Links to the Learning for Life and Work: Local and Global Citizenship requirements for Northern Ireland

Diversity and inclusion

Starter activity

Ask students to name as many local places of worship as they can. Which religions do they represent?

Resource sheets and Activity sheets

Students could work in pairs to identify the buildings on the Resource sheet, 'One city', using the clues on the Activity sheet, 'A multi-faith community'. You may want to go through the news articles on this sheet as a class.

The Resource sheet, 'Different cultures', focuses on some of the things which make up our culture but may not be directly related to race or religion. This sheet needs to be used with the Activity sheet, 'What is culture?'. At this point you might find it useful to talk about 'youth culture' and what this means.

The Activity sheet, 'Working together', is quite challenging and you may need to go through the words of the Act of Commitment in detail, explaining some of the more difficult words and giving concrete examples of what they might mean before students are ready to do the collage. Students could draw pictures or use images from magazines or the Internet to create their collages.

Plenary

The Act of Commitment ends with the words 'to help bring about a better world now and for generations to come'. Ask students if there is one thing they could do today to help bring about a better world. Set them the challenge of doing that one thing.

Background

The UK has a diverse range of people with different ethnic and cultural backgrounds. According to the 2001 census, 71% of the UK population considers themselves to be Christian, while 5% belong to other religions and 15% belong to no religion. Ninety-two per cent of the population describe themselves as white, 2% as black, 4.4% as Chinese or Asian and 1.2% as having a mixed ethnic background. Whilst ethnicity and religion clearly influence culture, there are many other influences, for example, regional area, rural or urban location and age.

One city

Places of worship in Bristol

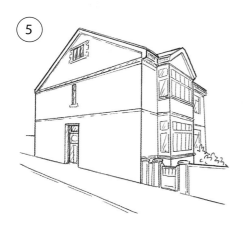

Diversity and values

Activity sheet – A multicultural, multi-faith society

A multi-faith community

Any large town in the UK will have groups of people from many different religions. Bristol has over 150 buildings where people meet to worship. A few of them are shown on the Resource sheet, 'One City'.

☞ 1 Use the clues below to work out which building is which. Write the number of the correct building in the box at the end of each clue.

The Anglican cathedral has two square towers.

The Jamia mosque has five pointed windows.

The Hindu temple is in an old church.

The Buddhist centre is in a house.

The Jewish synagogue has a large arched doorway.

The Catholic cathedral has tall points in the centre.

The Sikh temple has lots of windows.

Now read the two newspaper articles below. Both are true, but their headlines give very different pictures of the UK.

Britain still a Christian Country

Christianity is the official religion of the UK and the Queen is the Head of the Church of England. Over 70% of the population describes themselves as Christian.

Britain now a multi-faith country

There are people from almost every world religion living in the UK. Many are Christian but over 3,000,000 people follow other religions.

☞ 2 Would you describe Britain as multi-faith or Christian? Give reasons for your answer using a separate sheet of paper.

Different cultures

I want to
do well at school.
My parents say that
education is the way to a
better life.

I expect my
children to move out when
they become adults. My mother lives in
an old people's home.

My grandmother
lives with us and so do
my sister and her husband
and son.

My parents
didn't think school
was very important. I left
as soon as I could to
get a job.

I don't
really talk to
boys. I only feel comfortable
with boys from my own
family.

We often meet
up with other families
in the pub to talk, sing and
play music together.

My friends
include boys and
girls.

We don't really
know our neighbours and
most of our friends live a long way
away but we do see them in the
holidays.

Diversity and values

Activity sheet – A multicultural, multi-faith society

What is culture?

Our culture is often linked to our religion and where we come from, but culture is about other things as well. The words below show some of the things which make up our culture.

☞ 1 Read the Resource sheet, 'Different cultures'. Circle the words or phrases below which show what each pair are talking about. The first one has been done for you.

friends   celebrations and festivals   (family)

food

education

art and literature   hobbies and interests

music

community   clothes and jewellery

manners

faiths and beliefs   customs

☞ 2 Design a poster about your own culture. Use the words in the box above to give you ideas for the things you could include.

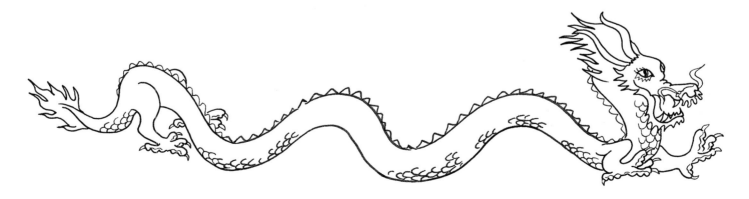

Working together

On 3 January 2000, members of many different faiths held a service together in London. During the service they made a commitment to work together. The words they spoke are given below.

☞ 1 Read the words and talk about what each section means.

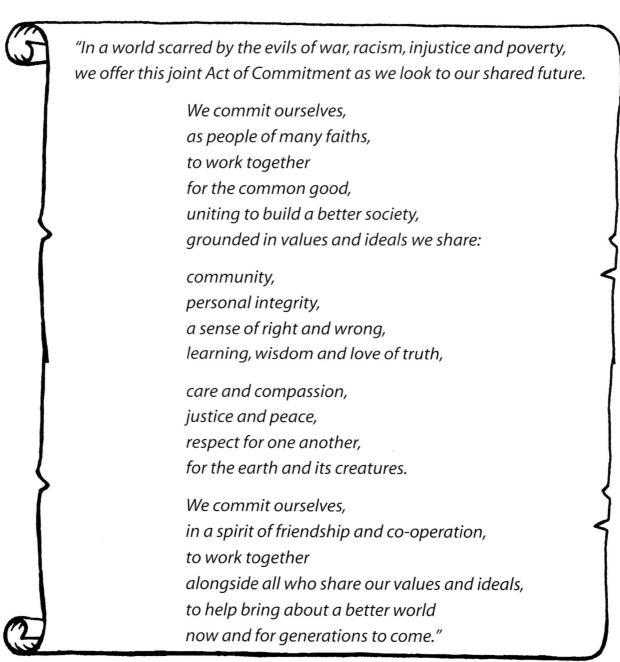

"In a world scarred by the evils of war, racism, injustice and poverty, we offer this joint Act of Commitment as we look to our shared future.

We commit ourselves,
as people of many faiths,
to work together
for the common good,
uniting to build a better society,
grounded in values and ideals we share:

community,
personal integrity,
a sense of right and wrong,
learning, wisdom and love of truth,

care and compassion,
justice and peace,
respect for one another,
for the earth and its creatures.

We commit ourselves,
in a spirit of friendship and co-operation,
to work together
alongside all who share our values and ideals,
to help bring about a better world
now and for generations to come."

☞ 2 Create a collage with all or some of the words of the Act of Commitment at the centre. The pictures for your collage should reflect the ideas in the commitment.

Diversity and values

Teacher's notes

Age and ability

Objectives

- To think about the needs of people with different abilities, disabilities and ages
- Reflect on some of the prejudices different groups face
- To think about ways that people's needs can be met and prejudices can be broken down

Prior knowledge

Students require no prior knowledge for this unit.

Links to the PSHE: Personal Well-being KS3 Programme of Study for England

1.1 Personal identities
1.5 Diversity

Links to the Draft Curriculum for Excellence for Scotland

Health and Well-being: Relationships
Social Studies: People, past events and societies

Links to the Personal and Social Education Framework for Wales

Community aspect
Social aspect

Links to the Learning for Life and Work: Local and Global Citizenship requirements for Northern Ireland

Diversity and inclusion

Starter activity

Ask students to put their hands up if they have spoken to someone over the age of 80 this week. How many of those were not family members?

Resource sheets and Activity sheets

You should read the news article on the Activity sheet, 'We can mix', with the whole class and talk about why the over 60's sports club wasn't allowed to meet in the holidays and whether or not that was fair. Encourage students to look at both sides of the argument. Students could write the letters individually, or they could work in pairs, with one person writing as a member of the older team and the other as a member of the younger team.

The first task on the Activity sheet, 'The young and the old', could be done as a class brainstorm. This will need careful handling as some of the prejudices they suggest might be offensive. Students could then design their posters individually, perhaps for homework.

The Resource sheet, 'Getting to know me' and the Activity sheet, 'Abilities and needs', looks at the idea that treating people fairly does not necessarily mean treating everyone the same.

The Activity sheet, 'Town planning', would make a good end of term activity.

Plenary

Students could make suggestions for ways in which the school could be made more inclusive. These suggestions could be put to the school council or governors for consideration.

Background

We are certainly moving towards a more inclusive society, for example, we no longer have huge institutions to segregate people with learning disabilities, but many groups still face prejudice and a lack of understanding of their needs. Educational and recreational activities tend to be segregated by age, and many young people will seldom meet elderly people outside of their own families. According to recent statistics, there will soon be more people over 80 than under 5 in the UK (source: Malcolm Wicks MP, Minister of State for Pensions).

We can mix

THE BINTON GAZETTE

20p

526 years of sporting talent

Two teams with a combined age of 526 competed in a unique inter-age challenge this week at Binton Sports Centre. Chairperson of the Over 60's club, Yvonne Partner says, "We are a thriving club with over 50 members, who meet on Monday and Thursday mornings but we were only allowed to use the sports centre during term-time. We felt this was unfair and wanted to show the centre that we were quite happy to mix with the youngsters. We persuaded them to let the club meet as normal during half-term, and we all got on so well that we thought we'd hold a competition."

The club chose a team of six people whose ages were 82, 74, 62, 69, 71 and 78. The youngsters fielded a team of six aged 14 to 16. Team 'Oldies' played team 'Youngsters', at bowls, table tennis, badminton, swimming, darts and squash.

The Oldies won the bowls and the table tennis but the Youngsters won the challenge overall by 4 to 2. Youngsters captain Jon Moore said, "We had a fantastic time. The other team

Team captains

nearly beat us at darts and squash but in the end our fitness won the day. Their supporters made a lot more noise than ours though!"

The sports centre has now changed their policy, and the Over 60's club will be allowed to meet throughout the year. The inter-age challenge is likely to become an annual event. Pete Miles, 82, says, "I'm going to have to brush-up on my badminton for next year."

☞ Read the newspaper article above. Imagine you were one of the team members of either the Oldies or the Youngsters. Write a letter to a friend telling them about the event. Try to include your thoughts and how your ideas changed as you got to know the other team.

Activity sheet – Age and ability

The young and the old

☞ 1 Make a list of places where young and old people regularly meet in your area. Are there many or do they tend to lead separate lives?

☞ 2 Old people and young people can both face prejudice. Complete the boxes below with some of the negative things people sometimes say about young and old people.

Prejudices about old people	Prejudices about young people
They moan a lot	They cause trouble
They think they know best	They're rude

These prejudices are based on stereotypes. They may be true of a few old or young people, but they are not true of all old and young people.

☞ 3 Design a poster showing either the good things about older people, or the good things about younger people. The aim of your poster is to convince people that the stereotypes are not true.

Getting to know me

"My name is Craig. I am 13 and I have Asperger's syndrome. This means that I don't always fit in with the other kids in my school. I like things to be very organised and I don't like to be touched. I managed at primary school because everyone knew me but when I started at secondary school it was terrible. I couldn't stand moving from lesson to lesson as I got pushed about, it was noisy and I didn't know where I was going.

Lessons were hard too. I didn't always understand when the teacher's made jokes. Once I got into trouble because the teacher said, 'Anyone who doesn't want a detention better get their head down fast' and I put my head on the desk and got shouted at for being cheeky when I wasn't being. I got teased a lot, well, bullied really, for being different.

Luckily I had an outreach worker who helped me. She talked to the teachers so they understood more about me and she helped me give a talk to my form group too. Now I am allowed to go three minutes early to lessons so I avoid the crush in the corridors and the other kids understand me better. I have a group of mates and we all talk about computer games. I've got a great memory so I'm always telling them about cheats and short cuts I've read about. Things are much better now that people know me."

Activity sheet – Age and ability

Abilities and needs

Read the Resource sheet, 'Getting to know me'. Do you think it's fair that Craig is allowed to leave his lessons early?

Treating people fairly doesn't always mean treating them in the same way. Karl goes to the same school as Craig. Read his story.

I'm the county under-15's tennis champion. My ambition is to win one of the big titles like Wimbledon. I train four times a week and run or do weight training twice a week. I do lots of competitions, sometimes abroad, and it means I miss quite a bit of school. I'm doing my GCSEs this year so I have to make up the work I miss. I take work away with me. Also, I don't do PE at school; instead, I go to the library and work. I'm doing one GCSE less than my mates so I do private study then too. Some people complain that I get time off when they're not allowed it for holidays and things but dad says to ignore them. He says I have a special talent and it would be wrong not to try to develop it.

Is it fair that Craig is allowed to take time off school?

One of the parents of the school has written to the head teacher to complain that Craig and Karl are treated differently from their child.

☞ On a separate piece of paper write the head teacher's reply. You should explain why you feel it is right to make these special arrangements.

Activity sheet – Age and ability

Town planning

You are the architect for a new town project. You have already designed houses, schools and shops. Now you need to design an outside play and relaxation area which can be used by everybody in the community.

☞ 1 Complete the planning boxes below. Some ideas have been included to get you started.

How do you want people to feel in this area?

Happy, safe, relaxed,

What groups will use the area?

Teenagers, parents and toddlers, wheelchair users,

What facilities will you need?

Toilets, seating, swings,

☞ 2 Now design the area. You could include notes on your design to show what you have included and why.

Diversity and values

Teacher's notes

Gender and sexual orientation

Objectives

- Look at the continuing gender divide in choices at post-16
- To explore attitudes towards gay and lesbian students and their experiences within schools

Prior knowledge

Students will need to understand that people can have different sexual orientations.

Links to the PSHE: Personal Well-being KS3 Programme of Study for England

1.1 Personal identities
1.5 Diversity

Links to the Draft Curriculum for Excellence for Scotland

Health and Well-being: Relationships
Social Studies: People, past events and societies

Links to the Personal and Social Education Framework for Wales

Community aspect
Social aspect

Links to the Learning for Life and Work: Local and Global Citizenship requirements for Northern Ireland

Diversity and inclusion

Background

Despite government campaigns and the introduction of the National Curriculum, which means that boys and girls now study very similar subjects up until the age of 16, the gender gap is still huge at post 16. The gender gap continues into employment too; in 2007 the Equal Opportunities Commission reported that just 10% of the directors of the FTSE 100 companies were women. Although tackling bullying has been high on the agenda for most schools, a survey by Stonewall found that 98% of gay and lesbian students reported hearing the term 'gay' used in a derogatory fashion at school, and only 23% had been told that homophobic bullying was wrong by their schools.

Starter activity

Ask students if they would prefer to go to an all boys, all girls or mixed school. Look at the reasons behind their answers.

Resource sheets and Activity sheets

The Resource and Activity sheets, 'It was different in my day' and 'Then and now', look at gender issues within education.

Students could complete the table on, 'Then and now', in pairs or small groups but it would probably be best to discuss the questions relating to current choices at 16 as a class. You could collate a list of reasons on the board of why girls and boys make different choices and ask for suggestions to how this could be changed. The poster activity could be done individually and could be set as homework.

The Activity sheet, 'I might quit', looks at problems girls face when choosing traditionally male careers. You could also look at a situation where a boy chooses a traditionally female career, such as hairdressing. Students could write the letters from Aunty Sadie individually or in pairs. Alternatively you might suggest that Aunty Sadie decides to ring Genna up and pairs of students could role play their telephone conversation.

Students will need to read the Resource sheet, 'In the chat room', before working through the Activity sheet, 'Don't label me'. You could have a class vote to choose the best leaflet design which could then be scanned, printed and distributed around the school.

Plenary

Stonewall is a group whose aims include tackling homophobic bullying in schools and the workplace. Their poster campaign included a large poster containing only the words 'Some people are gay. Get over it.' Write this slogan on the board and ask students whether or not it is effective. Challenge them to come up with other slogans which teach tolerance and respect.

It was different in my day

"I loved school but it was very different from schools today. My school in the 1950s had boys and girls but we were taught in different classes. Everyone did English and Maths and then the girls did Needlework, Cookery, Art and Music while the boys did Metalwork, Woodwork, Physics and Chemistry. Girls could also do French and History or Shorthand and Typing. I think the boys did Bookkeeping. While I was there, some girls campaigned to be allowed to do Science. Eventually they were allowed to do Biology, but not Physics or Chemistry.

Boys and girls had separate playgrounds and when I first started we ate separately but later we ate together. Boys wore shorts in the lower years, then trousers. Girls wore pinafore dresses and then skirts. None of the female staff wore trousers. If things needed carrying, like desks moving for exams, the boys were always sent to do it, never the girls.

PE was separate with the girls playing netball, hockey and rounders and the boys playing football, cricket and rugby. We all did cross-country but not at the same time. I remember being told I was a 'hussy' by Miss Blake because I was watching the boys playing cricket out of the window during French once.

Boys and girls got detentions or lines, but boys got punished more often. For serious misbehaviour the girls would be smacked across the knuckles with a ruler and the boys got the cane."

Activity sheet – Gender and sexual orientation

Then and now

☞ 1 Read Elsie's account of school during the 1950s on the Resource sheet, 'It was different in my day'. Then copy and complete the chart below showing how boys and girls were treated differently in the 1950s.

School life in the 1950s	
Boys	Girls
• Taught in boys classes • Metal, Woodwork, Physics and Chemistry	• Taught in girls classes • Needlework, Cookery, Art and Music

Do schools treat boys and girls differently today?

The National Curriculum means boys and girls study the same subjects today, but they still make very different choices at 16. Look at the facts below.

> 96% of students doing an engineering apprenticeship are boys.

> 77% of students studying A level Physics are boys.

> 92% of students studying hairdressing and beauty courses are girls.

> 70% of students studying A level English are girls.

Why do you think boys and girls make different choices at 16?

☞ 2 Design a poster aimed at persuading either boys to study French or Hairdressing, or girls to study Physics or Engineering.

Activity sheet – Gender and sexual orientation

I might quit

Genna's aunt is a mechanic and Genna has started training as a mechanic too but things aren't going well. Read the letter Genna has written to her aunt.

Dear Aunty Sadie,

How are you? Better than me I hope. I've been doing my mechanics course now for six weeks and I hate it. It's not the work, I love what we're learning and all the practical work on the vehicles, it's the people. The other nine students are all boys and they don't know how to treat me. Some of them try to flirt with me some keep thumping me on the back, and one keeps asking me if I'm a lesbian! Even the instructors treat me differently. Today one gave me his chair even though half the boys were standing. The older instructor calls the boys by their surname but he calls me 'Miss Genna'. Sometimes when I come in the room they all shut up. I really hate being the odd one out and I'm thinking of quitting. What should I do?

With love from one very fed up Genna X

Aunty Sadie thinks Genna should carry on with the course.

☞ On a separate piece of paper write Aunty Sadie's reply in which she gives Genna advice and encourages her to keep going. Think about the reasons she might give before you start writing.

Resource sheet – Gender and sexual orientation

In the chat room

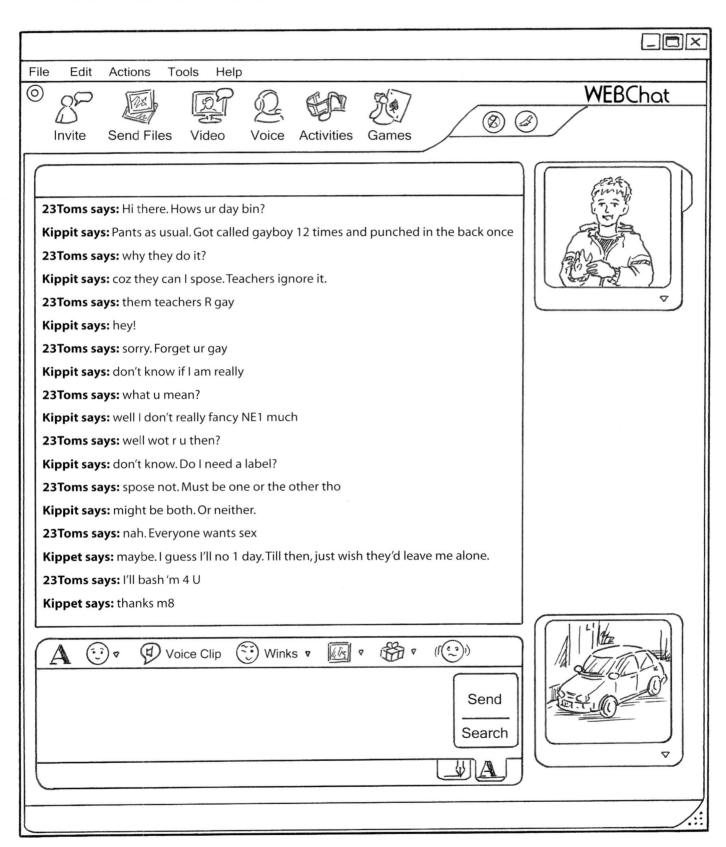

File   Edit   Actions   Tools   Help

Invite   Send Files   Video   Voice   Activities   Games

WEBChat

23Toms says: Hi there. Hows ur day bin?

Kippit says: Pants as usual. Got called gayboy 12 times and punched in the back once

23Toms says: why they do it?

Kippit says: coz they can I spose. Teachers ignore it.

23Toms says: them teachers R gay

Kippit says: hey!

23Toms says: sorry. Forget ur gay

Kippit says: don't know if I am really

23Toms says: what u mean?

Kippit says: well I don't really fancy NE1 much

23Toms says: well wot r u then?

Kippit says: don't know. Do I need a label?

23Toms says: spose not. Must be one or the other tho

Kippit says: might be both. Or neither.

23Toms says: nah. Everyone wants sex

Kippet says: maybe. I guess I'll no 1 day. Till then, just wish they'd leave me alone.

23Toms says: I'll bash 'm 4 U

Kippet says: thanks m8

A   Voice Clip   Winks

Send

Search

Don't label me

Read the chat room conversation on the Resource sheet, 'In the chat room'.

In their conversation, 23Toms said that Kippet had to be either gay, straight, both or neither. We often feel the need to label people, but not everyone wants to be labelled. Read the comments below.

I'm pretty sure I'm gay but I have a friend who says I should just take my time and see how I feel. He says I don't need to label myself yet.

When I was younger if you were gay you had to act 'gay'. I wore pink because my gay friends did. Now I know being gay just says who I'm attracted to. It doesn't say anything else about me. I'm lots of other things besides being gay.

I've always known I'm a lesbian but I choose not to tell most people. After all, straight people don't go round telling everyone they're straight.

I announced that I was a lesbian when I was 15 and I've been telling everyone ever since. I just find it easier that way.

Kippet is obviously having a hard time at school. Homophobic bullying, where people are teased or bullied about being gay or lesbian, is very common in schools.

☞ Design a leaflet aimed at stopping homophobic bullying in your school.

Diversity and values

Teacher's notes

How the UK was made

Objectives

- To understand some of the geographical and political origins of the UK
- To understand that the nation of the UK is made up of four different countries, each with its own identity
- Begin to understand the complexity of national identity

Prior knowledge

Students should know that the world is divided into countries.

Links to the PSHE: Personal Well-being KS3 Programme of Study for England

1.1 Personal identities
1.5 Diversity

Links to the Draft Curriculum for Excellence for Scotland

Health and Well-being: Relationships
Social Studies: People, past events and societies

Links to the Personal and Social Education Framework for Wales

Community aspect
Social aspect

Links to the Learning for Life and Work: Local and Global Citizenship requirements for Northern Ireland

Diversity and inclusion

Background

The UK has been formed by a variety of geographical, historical and political events. England, Wales, Scotland and Northern Ireland are often considered as separate countries, but these four countries make up the nation state of the UK. The official name of the UK is 'The United Kingdom of Great Britain and Northern Ireland'. Strictly speaking, Great Britain is the land mass of Wales, Scotland and England, while the British Isles refers to all the islands of Great Britain and Ireland. 'Britain' and 'the UK' are informal names given to The United Kingdom of Great Britain and Northern Ireland. All of these terms are frequently used inaccurately. Many people abroad refer to England when in fact they mean the UK.

Starter activity

Ask students which country they live in. Discuss the different possible answers (for example, England, Great Britain, The UK and so on) and establish definitions for each.

Resource sheets and Activity sheets

The Activity sheet, 'An island apart', and the Resource sheet, 'Four become one', give a very brief outline of the major geographical and political events which have formed the UK. Students are not always aware that country borders can change and it can be useful to point out that nations are not permanent fixtures. You might refer to recent changes in Eastern Europe and the former USSR as a further example of this. You could also highlight the fact that the human race did not begin in the UK and that therefore everyone who lives here is descended from someone who travelled here in the near or distant past.

The statements on, 'Does Nationality matter?', cover some quite complex issues and you might like to discuss them as a class before asking students to fill in the table. You could also look back at their answers after they have read the Resource sheet, 'What nationality am I?', to see if their ideas have changed. As nationality can be a sensitive issue, students should be given the option of keeping their statement on their own nationality confidential if they wish to.

Plenary

Ask students to complete the sentence, 'Nationality is/is not important because…' Discuss their answers.

Activity sheet – How the UK was made

An island apart

The UK hasn't always been here in the way it is now.

☞ Use the words in the fourth box to fill in the gaps of this account of how the United Kingdom was formed.

1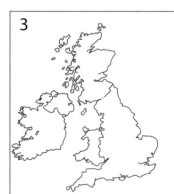

Scientists think that 180 _____ years ago all the countries of the world were bunched together in one huge supercontinent called Pangaea. Very slowly, the land drifted apart to form the _____ we know today.

2

For a long _____ Britain remained attached to Europe. People lived in _____ and _____ groups. They moved around looking for food and better places to live. Some of them _____ as far as the UK.

3

About 8,500 years ago _____ sea levels cut Great Britain off from the continent. The UK took the shape that we know _____.

---

continents	family	walked	today
time	tribes	rising	million

Diversity and values   © Folens (copiable page)

Resource sheet – How the UK was made

Four become one

The UK is made up of four countries. The picture below shows how this came about.

Scotland

For many centuries Scotland had its own kings. In 1603 the English Queen, Elizabeth I, died. She had no children so she left the English throne to King James VI of Scotland. For the first time England and Wales, Scotland and Ireland all had the same king, although they were still three separate countries. In 1707 Scotland was officially joined to England and Wales, creating the United Kingdom of Great Britain.

Wales

Wales was ruled by several princes. In 1282 the King of England (Edward I) invaded Wales and brought it under English rule.

England

England was once made up of different tribes. Gradually, leaders began to rule larger areas. By the eleventh century most of England was united under one king.

Northern Ireland

Ireland had a number of rulers and kings, then in 1542 King Henry VIII (of England and Wales) declared himself King of Ireland as well. In 1801 Ireland officially joined the UK. In 1922 the Republic of Ireland became a separate state and the official title of the UK became 'The United Kingdom of Great Britain and Northern Ireland'.

What nationality am I?

I used to say I was British but since working in Wales I've started to say I'm English. The Welsh people seem proud of being Welsh and 'British' seems a bit of a nothingness compared to that.

My parents are Scottish but we live in England. When we visit Scotland the people there call me the 'wee English Lassie'. I feel more British than Scottish, but I think my parents would be sad about that.

I'm Cornish through and through.

My parents are both from Bangladesh but I am British. I have far more in common with my British friends than I do with my relatives on the other side of the world.

I'm Welsh but I say I'm from the UK, especially if I'm on the Internet. People from other countries don't understand the whole Welsh/British thing.

I'm from Northern Ireland. I have joint British and Irish citizenship but I feel Irish. Ireland is an island, the fact that it's split into two different countries makes no sense to me.

I'm a Scot. I don't have anything against the English but I don't feel I have much in common with them either.

Diversity and values

Activity sheet – How the UK was made

Does nationality matter?

☞ 1 Read the statements below and tick to show whether you 'agree', 'disagree' or are 'not sure' about them. You may need to discuss some of the ideas before you can decide what you think.

	agree	disagree	not sure
Your nationality is based on where you are born.			
Your nationality is based on the nationality of your parents.			
You should be able to choose your own nationality.			
Nationality and ethnic origin is not the same thing.			
It doesn't matter what nationality you are.			
People should be proud of their nationality.			

Now read the Resource sheet, 'What nationality am I?'. All the people are British, but they don't all describe themselves as British.

☞ 2 Make a list of the different words they use to describe their nationality.

On a separate piece of paper write a statement about yourself which describes your nationality as you see it. You don't have to show your statement to anyone else if you don't want to.

Teacher's notes

The UK in Europe

Objectives

- To understand that the UK is part of the European Union (EU)
- To gain a basic understanding of the aims of the EU
- To become more familiar with the EU countries
- To begin to look at the role of EU workers in the UK

Prior knowledge

Students require no prior knowledge for this unit.

Links to the PSHE: Personal Well-being KS3 Programme of Study for England

1.1 Personal identities
1.5 Diversity

Links to the Draft Curriculum for Excellence for Scotland

Health and Well-being: Relationships
Social Studies: People, past events and societies

Links to the Personal and Social Education Framework for Wales

Community aspect
Social aspect

Links to the Learning for Life and Work: Local and Global Citizenship requirements for Northern Ireland

Diversity and inclusion

Background

There is a great deal of news coverage focusing on Eastern European workers coming to the UK. A report published by the TUC in 2007 refuted many of the claims often found in the tabloid press. The report argued that, while some local services were put under stress, migrant workers were responsible for about 10% of Britain's economic growth and contributed more in taxes than the value they received in public services (source: the economics of migration, TUC 2007).

Starter activity

Hold a quick competition to see which group can write down the most European countries in five minutes.

Resource sheets and Activity sheets

The Activity sheet, 'What is the European Union?', can be used as an introduction to the topic. Students could fill in the gaps, and you could then read the whole text with the class and discuss it.

The Activity sheet, 'Who's in the EU?', lists the countries who are members of the EU. The capital letter of each country has been left as a capital in the anagrams to make the unscrambling easier and to reinforce the rule that country names always start with a capital. You could give the class a time limit to complete as many as possible, checking their answers against the EU website *http://europa.eu/index_en.htm*. Students could colour in the flags in the appropriate colours during the lesson or as homework.

The Resource sheet, 'Go where you want' and the Activity sheet, 'Where would you go?', stress the point that EU citizens are free to live, work and study in any EU country (although there are still some restrictions on the movement of people from some of the countries which have recently joined the EU). You could allocate different countries to pairs of students and ask them to research them and report back to the class. Students may need to look back at their list of EU countries to make sure they choose a country that is in the EU.

The Activity sheet, 'Europeans in the UK', looks at the movement of labour within the EU. The essential point to highlight is that wages are much higher in Britain for unskilled workers than in many Eastern European countries, but that there is a shortage of UK workers willing to fill the posts. This is because the wages are low by UK standards, or because there is a shortage in some areas, such as medical workers and teachers.

Plenary

The origins of the EU came out of a desire to forge strong trade links which would make war between the member states unlikely. Ask students whether they think stronger links with other countries would make war less likely and why.

Activity sheet – The UK in Europe

What is the European Union?

☞ Use the words in the box at the bottom of the page to fill in the gaps and find out about the European Union.

The European Union is a group of 27 _____ who have agreed to work together to try to make Europe a good place for people to live in. It is called the EU for short. The UK is _____ of the EU.

Movement and trade between EU countries has been made as easy as possible so that people can _____ about and do business together. Many EU countries use the same currency, called the _____, which makes it especially easy for businesses and people to buy and _____ between countries.

The EU makes laws but each country has its _____ laws too. A country's own laws have to agree with the laws of the EU. The EU tries to make sure that EU countries are governed _____.

The EU tries to help its _____ countries so that everyone in the EU can have a good standard of living. People in EU countries can choose to work and _____ in any EU country.

The EU _____ to provide _____ food, a _____ environment, better living standards and joint action on crime.

part	sell	fairly
Euro	own	aims
countries	live	travel
greener	poorer	safer

Who's in the EU?

☞ Unscramble the letters below to find the 27 EU countries.

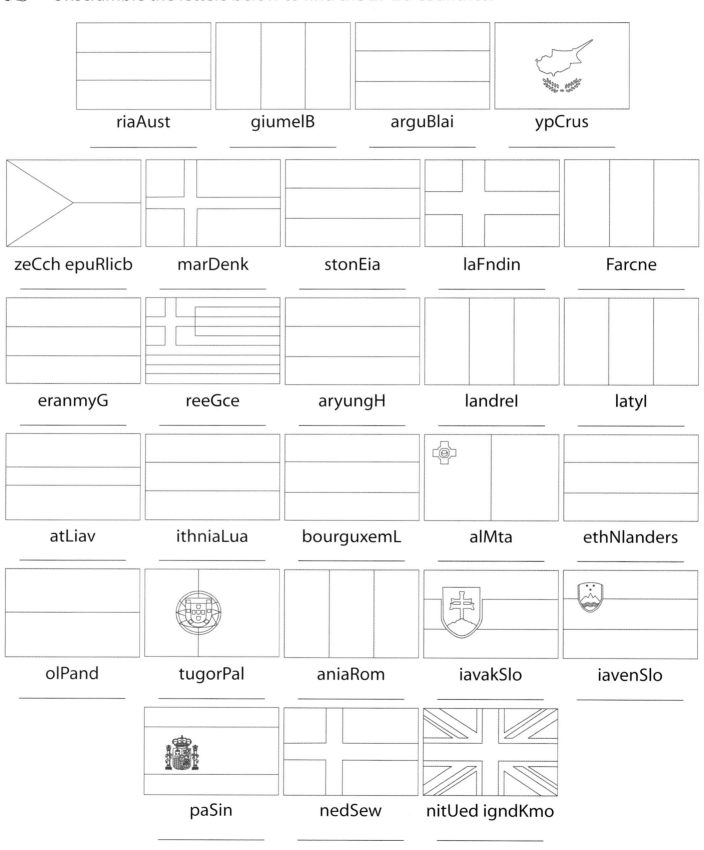

riaAust	giumelB	arguBlai	ypCrus
zeCch epuRlicb	marDenk	stonEia	laFndin	Farcne
eranmyG	reeGce	aryungH	landrel	latyl
atLiav	ithniaLua	bourguxemL	alMta	ethNlanders
olPand	tugorPal	aniaRom	iavakSlo	iavenSlo
	paSin	nedSew	nitUed igndKmo	

Diversity and values

Go where you want

Erica

I went to stay with friends in France for a months holiday. I was planning to come back to the UK to train as a nurse. While I was in France I started helping out in the care home where my friend's mum worked. I really enjoyed it and they offered me a job so I stayed on. Another girl and I rented a flat and I worked at the care home for a year. By then, my French was so good that I decided to do my nurse's training here so now I'm living in Paris training to be a nurse. Because France is an EU country there's been no problem about me staying, working or studying here. It's fantastic. I've nearly finished my training now and I might go and work in Belgium next year.

I live in the South of England and I work for a builder. He gets lots of jobs doing up Spanish villas for English people who are moving out there. We go over and stay in the villas while we work on them. It's fantastic. My boss is thinking of moving out to Spain and working there all the time. If he does, I might go out there too.

Phil

Activity sheet – The UK in Europe

Where would you go?

Read the Resource sheet, 'Go where you want'. Because France and Spain are both in the EU, it is easy for Erica and Phil to work and live there.

☞ 1 Why might people choose to work abroad? List your ideas on the flag below.

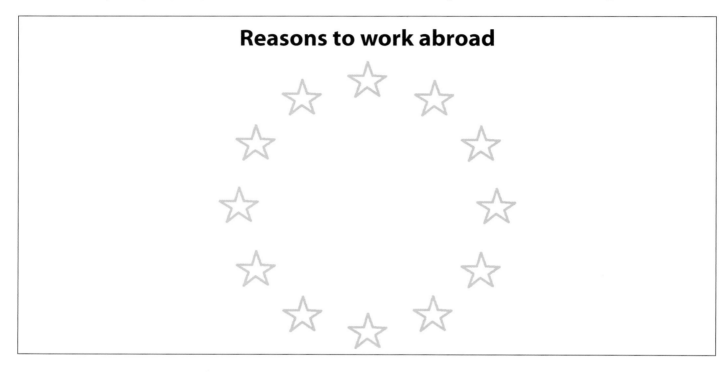

As a British citizen, you can choose to work, live and study in any EU country. Imagine you have decided to move to another EU country for a while. What might you enjoy and what might you find difficult?

☞ 2 Fill in the information below. You may need to do some research to find out about the country you have chosen before you begin.

I would choose to live in _____.

The things I think I would like about this country are: _____

_____

_____

The things I might find difficult are: _____

_____

_____

Diversity and values

Activity sheet – The UK in Europe

Europeans in the UK

People from the UK are free to live, work and study in any EU country, and many people from other EU countries are free to live, work and study in the UK. Read the comments below.

My name is Aric and I am from Poland. I came over to the UK to work for a building firm three years ago because the pay in the UK was much better. Things have picked up in Poland now and I will probably be going home soon, but I've enjoyed working in Britain.

My name is Orla and I'm from Ireland. There aren't many teaching jobs in Ireland at the moment and there's a shortage of teachers in the UK so I came to the UK to work. There's no problem with the language and I love it here so I might stay.

I am Gergana from Bulgaria. A company came to Sofia where I live advertising jobs in care homes in the UK. I was experienced and qualified so I got a job. I work with old people in a home in Norwich. It's a much nicer home than the one I worked in in Sofia.

My name is Valdis and I live in Riga, Latvia. I come over to the UK for about six months every year to work on farms around the country. I think the pay is too low to attract British workers. During the winter, I go back to Riga where I have a job as a storeman. This way I am able to provide a better standard of living for my family.

☞ List the reasons the four people give for wanting to work in the UK.

_____   _____

_____   _____

Why don't British people want to do some of the jobs which other EU workers do? Explain your answer below.

_____

_____

Teacher's notes

Immigration issues

Objectives

- To recognise the bias in some news reporting regarding immigration issues
- To understand that people have emigrated throughout history
- To understand the range of reasons why people emigrate
- To consider how our sense of self is influenced by the cultures to which we belong

Prior knowledge

Students require a basic understanding that people from different countries sometimes move around the world.

Links to the PSHE: Personal Well-being KS3 Programme of Study for England

1.1 Personal identities
1.5 Diversity

Links to the Draft Curriculum for Excellence for Scotland

Health and Well-being: Relationships
Social Studies: People, past events and societies

Links to the Personal and Social Education Framework for Wales

Community aspect
Social aspect

Links to the Learning for Life and Work: Local and Global Citizenship requirements for Northern Ireland

Diversity and inclusion

Background

According to the 2001 UK census, 8.3% of the total population of the UK were born abroad. Of those born abroad, 33% were born in Europe. In recent years, workers from EU countries have moved to Britain, although it is unclear how many of these intend to return to their country of birth. Much media coverage of immigration is negative, some of it stridently so.

Starter activity

Explain the term immigration and then ask students who were the first people to live in Britain. If you have covered the unit, 'How the UK was made', students may remember that the UK was populated by tribes moving across Europe. If not, you may have to tell them. Point out that, historically, we are all descended from immigrants.

Resource sheets and Activity sheets

The Activity sheet, 'Biased reporting', encourages students to look for the facts behind media stories. You could bring in a selection of newspapers and look at stories relating to immigration to look for examples of bias. You may need to talk about the meanings of the words 'immigration', 'immigrant' and 'emigrate'. It is worth pointing out to students that immigration has two m's, but emigrates only has one.

The Resource sheet, 'Afrah's story' and the Activity sheet, 'I'm multicultural', then focus on the experiences of people moving to the UK. After some class discussion students could work in small groups to plan and act out their radio programmes.

The Activity sheet, 'It's not new', looks at how different groups of immigrants have moved to the UK over the years. If your own area has a rich history of immigration students could design a local logo as well.

Students could read the comments on the Activity sheet, 'Why do people emigrate?', in small groups and write their lists, before comparing their ideas as a class. It is important to stress that some people are forced to emigrate, while others are able to choose. The web page could be done on a computer or simply as a web page design, with text, on paper.

Plenary

Ask how many students have ever moved house within the UK. List some of the reasons they moved on the board. Are some of the reasons people move within the UK similar to the reasons why people move *to* the UK?

Diversity and values

Activity sheet – Immigration issues

Biased reporting

In the UK immigration is often reported in a sensational way. It can be difficult to tell the facts from the myths. All of the statements in the column on the left below are misleading.

 1 Match them with the statements on the right which give the facts. The first one has been done for you.

BRITAIN SWAMPED BY IMMIGRANTS! ●	● Most immigrants get jobs in the UK and pay tax.
Britain has highest rate of immigration in Europe ●	● The UK relies on immigration to fill some jobs where there are shortages of UK workers.
IMMIGRANTS TAKE OUR JOBS! ●	● About 8% of the UK population was born abroad.
NHS cracking under pressure of immigration ●	● Many doctors, nurses and hospital workers are from abroad. Without them the NHS would grind to a halt.
Immigrants live off benefits ●	● France, Germany and the Netherlands have higher levels of immigration than the UK.

☞ 2 Sometimes the language used in news reports about immigration can be very negative. Underline all the words which sound negative in the news article below. What are the facts in this story?

GPs swamped by flood of foreigners

GP surgeries in Slough are under unbearable pressure thanks to the invasion of immigrants demanding free health care. Most surgeries in the area already have a full list of patients, but now they are expected to cope with hundreds more, with no extra help from the government. A receptionist at one surgery said, "Hordes of foreigners come in, who don't even speak English, expecting to get treatment. We haven't got space for any new patients."

Afrah's story

"My name is Afrah and I am 15. I was born in Yemen but my father already lived in England and my mother moved here with me when I was four. I have visited Yemen several times but I like living here best. Although girls go to school in Yemen now, the education is better here. I speak English, Arabic and some French. When I was in Primary school I used to have to translate for a new girl who only spoke Arabic but my mum complained as I was getting behind with my own work. Luckily the girl learnt to speak English quite quickly.

I have a friend in Yemen whose older brother has a mobile phone and I phone her sometimes. She is studying English and is hoping to be able to visit England one day. I stayed with her last summer and her mum taught me to cook. I helped with the animals and with the housework. We were allowed to go for walks but we were not allowed to speak to any boys. I wear the veil in Yemen because all the girls my age do and I don't want to be stared at but I don't wear it in England. In England, my parents don't mind me talking to boys but only in a group – they wouldn't want me to go out with a boy on my own. If I wanted, our friends in Yemen would find me a husband, but I don't want to and my parents want me to finish my education before I think about getting married. I want to go into childcare and am going to college to do an NVQ when I leave school."

Activity sheet – Immigration issues

I'm multicultural

☞ 1 Many people are happy belonging to two different cultures. Read the Resource sheet, 'Afrah's story'. How is her life in Yemen different from her life in the UK?

Read the comments below.

"Sometimes I feel left out at parties because I don't drink alcohol, but when I see the state some of my friends get into, I'm glad my parents have brought me up to have more self respect."

"I get cross when people ask if my parents are going to force me to have an arranged marriage. People think all Asian girls are forced to marry just because they've read about a few cases in the paper."

"I like being able to talk to my friends in a language the teachers don't understand. It drives them mad when they don't know what we're saying!"

"I offered to help a woman carry her shopping one day and she thought I was trying to rob her. In my country, a young man would always carry something for an elderly woman."

"I hate looking at newspapers. They seem to blame everything on immigrants."

"I dress traditionally when I visit my grandparents. My grandmother likes it and I feel special because I belong to her world as well as my own."

☞ 2 Using Afrah's story, the comments above, and any ideas of your own. Plan a radio show where people discuss the good and bad things about moving to the UK from abroad. Your show could include a discussion or a series of interviews.

It's not new

Immigration is not new. The area around Petticoat Lane market in London has been home to immigrants from all over the world since the seventeenth century. Each group brought skills and goods to the UK.

In the early seventeenth century Spanish courtiers visiting King James I settled in the area.

Later in the seventeenth century French Huguenot refugees brought their silk weaving and cloth making skills. Jewish refugees also settled in the area. Many of them were tailors or shoemakers.

In the nineteenth century more Jewish settlers arrived, fleeing from persecution in Europe. Irish people arrived too, to escape the potato famine in Ireland. Many worked as labourers helping to build roads, railways and the docks.

In the twentieth century, the area became a popular place for Asian immigrants to move to, particularly from Bangladesh and Bengal. Many of them worked in the market selling clothes.

Today the market is thriving. You can buy clothes, CDs, food, artwork and many other things.

☞ 1 Design a logo for Petticoat Lane market. Your logo should celebrate the history of the market.

☞ 2 Carry out research to find out about the history of immigration in your local area or region.

Diversity and values

Why do people emigrate?

Read the comments below.

"I was born in Uganda but my parents were from India. In 1972 the dictator Idi Amin gave all Asian's 90 days to leave the country. I came to the UK with my wife."

"I moved to the UK from Portugal because there was no work for me there."

"My parents moved to the UK from China. They wanted a better standard of living and they wanted my sisters and I to have a better education."

"My father sent me to the UK in 1999 when the Serbs were killing ethnic Albanians living in Kosovo. Later, my mother and my two brothers joined me, but my father was killed."

"I was born in Belgium. I met my husband, Paul, when he was visiting Belgium. We got married and moved to England."

"I lived in Iraq. When Saddam Hussein started killing the Kurds I spoke out against it. I was imprisoned, tortured and beaten. Eventually they let me go and I escaped to Iran and finally to the UK where I was given asylum status."

"I came to university in the UK from the USA. I liked it here so I stayed."

☞ 1 Make a list of reasons why people emigrate.

☞ 2 Design a web page aimed at children aged about eight explaining why people move to the UK.

Teacher's notes

Personal identity

Objectives

- To understand that identity is influenced by many factors
- Think about their own identity, and the things which influence it
- To appreciate the need for balance between feeling part of a group and retaining our own identity

Prior knowledge

No prior knowledge is required for this unit.

Links to the PSHE: Personal Well-being KS3 Programme of Study for England

1.1 Personal identities
1.5 Diversity

Links to the Draft Curriculum for Excellence for Scotland

Health and Well-being: Relationships
Social Studies: People, past events and societies

Links to the Personal and Social Education Framework for Wales

Community aspect
Social aspect

Links to the Learning for Life and Work: Local and Global Citizenship requirements for Northern Ireland

Diversity and inclusion

Background

Personal identity is a complex combination of nature and nurture. Most psychologists believe that the two are so interrelated that the question of which is most important is irrelevant. Families play a huge part in influencing the identity of young children, but as they grow older, young people are increasingly influenced by their peer groups.

Starter activity

Ask students to compare their fingerprints with the person next to them. What differences do they notice? How else is each person unique?

Resource sheets and Activity sheets

Begin by using the Activity sheet, 'Who am I?', to identify the different roles young people have. You could discuss as a class about whether or not we behave differently in our different roles.

Students could complete the table on the Activity sheet, 'What makes me me?', individually and then compare them in pairs. Encourage them to think about what difference, if any, there would be if one factor was completely changed. For example, would they be very different people if they had been born in the Victoria era or in the Stone Age?

The Activity sheet, 'Born or learnt?', looks at the 'nature verses nurture' debate. There may be adopted children in your class, and you will almost certainly have children with step-parents, so this can be a sensitive issue. You can talk about how we inherit physical characteristics from our birth parents and whether or not we inherit personality traits too.

Students could do the activity on the Activity sheet, 'How do I look?', in class or as homework. Their drawings can then be used as the basis for a discussion about how much we want to fit in with others and how much we want to be seen as individuals.

The Resource sheet, 'One of a crowd', also looks at the issue of fitting in versus being an individual. Students could discuss Tara's comments, or they could write her a letter giving her advice on how to deal with the situation.

Plenary

Choose a well-known football team and ask students to name some of the players. What do they have in common? How are they individuals? Our personal identity is a bit like being a member of a football team. We need to be able to work and play together, while making the most of our individual strengths and talents.

Activity sheet – Personal identity

Who am I?

We all have a number of different roles. Jordan has been writing down all of his roles.

☞ 1 Use a separate piece of paper to draw a picture of yourself and list your own roles.

son		brother
member of tutor group 8JMA		grandson
scout		nephew
neighbour		student
friend		member of a football team

☞ 2 Draw a circle around your three favourite roles. Are there any roles you don't like?

Activity sheet – Personal identity

What makes me me?

Many things affect the way we think and behave. The table below lists some of the things which might have helped make you who you are.

☞ 1 Tick, 'very much', 'a little' or 'not at all' for each item on the list to show which things have influenced you most.

	very much	a little	not at all
My parents			
The people I live with			
My wider family			
My friends			
My religion			
Where I was born			
The area I live in			
My country			
Music			
Famous people			
School			
Television and the media			
The times I live in			
Politicians			
Books			

☞ 2 Choose one of the items from the list above which you think has helped make you the person you are. Complete the sentence below to show how it has helped shape you.

_____ has/have helped make me the person I am today because

_____

_____

Diversity and values

Activity sheet – Personal identity

Born or learnt?

Aidan was adopted when he was a few weeks old. Read his comments below:

"My birth mother was very young when she had me and decided it would be best if I was adopted. I was brought up by my mum and dad and later they adopted my sister. My parents were quite well off and I went to a private school. We had great family holidays and I had a happy childhood. Now I'm training to be a dentist like my dad. Last year I traced my birth mother. She has been married twice and has two other children. She lives in a rough area of town and doesn't have much money so at first I thought we didn't have much in common. In fact I was a bit embarrassed because she thought I was so posh. Now I've got to know her though, I realise we're very alike. We both have the same sense of humour, we are both impatient and we tend to like the same people. My life would have been very different if I hadn't been adopted, but I think I would have been the same person."

Aidan thinks that his personality would have been the same, wherever he grew up. Do you think he is right?

 1 Circle four words in the box below that describes your personality. If you don't think any apply to you there is space to add your own ideas.

> cheerful, kind, shy, energetic, creative, out-going, friendly, relaxed, thoughtful, clever, imaginative, confident, nervous, ambitious, careful, funny, loyal, honest.

 2 Imagine you had been brought up in a very different place. Would these words still describe you?

Activity sheet – Personal identity

How do I look?

What we wear can say a lot about our personality. Simon has drawn himself in his favourite clothes and added labels to show what he thinks his clothes say about him.

☞ Read Simon's comments. On a separate piece of paper draw and label a picture of yourself showing what your clothes, hair, make-up and jewellery would say about you if you could choose to wear exactly what you wanted.

Long hair shows I'm laid back and chilled.

Surfer necklace because I want to learn to surf and travel to Australia.

T-shirt shows I'm into heavy metal bands.

Cheap trainers because I hate designer stuff.

When I'm old enough I'm going to have this tattoo because I'm a committed Christian.

One of a crowd

"My name is Tara and I'm 14. I have a great group of mates. There are five of us and we get on really well. We all like the same clothes and stuff. At school we always try to sit together and in the evenings we either meet up or talk online.

Recently though, the others have been making me feel bad about my clarinet lessons. I love playing the clarinet and I am in an orchestra which meets every Saturday morning. My mates usually go into town on Saturdays and they say I'm really missing out.

They're always talking about what they've done and laughing about stuff that I've missed. They think that the orchestra is for geeks and they've started to tease me about it. I don't want to give it up, but I don't want to be different from my friends either. I don't know what to do."

Teacher's notes

Personal values

Objectives

- To consider what values are
- Think about students' own personal values
- Think about how our actions reflect our values

Prior knowledge

Understand that different people have different beliefs and different ideas about what is important.

Links to the PSHE: Personal Well-being KS3 Programme of Study for England

1.1 Personal identities
1.5 Diversity

Links to the Draft Curriculum for Excellence for Scotland

Health and Well-being: Relationships
Social Studies: People, past events and societies

Links to the Personal and Social Education Framework for Wales

Community aspect
Social aspect

Links to the Learning for Life and Work: Local and Global Citizenship requirements for Northern Ireland

Diversity and inclusion

Background

Everyone has values, but the extent to which we act on our values varies. Also, what we say is not always the same as what we do. For example, few people would say that stealing was acceptable, yet many people will keep quiet when they are given the wrong change.

Starter activity

Ask students how we keep valuable things safe, for example, write a list, keep them somewhere safe, clean them, check on them, don't let others touch them. Keep the list for the plenary session.

Resource sheets and Activity sheets

The symbol designing activity on the Activity sheet, 'What do you value?', is designed to encourage students to think about what the words stand for. Some, like family and friendship, will be straightforward, but others will require more thought. The concepts here are quite abstract, but the next two sheets look at them in more concrete terms.

Of the four cartoons on the Resource sheet, 'Values in every day life', the first deals with honesty, the second with trust, the third with family and the fourth with fairness. You could argue that they all deal with loyalty and friendship. This sheet needs to be used in conjunction with the Activity sheet, 'What would you do?'. Encourage students to see that our personal values are evidenced in our everyday decisions.

The Activity sheet, 'Values in action', looks at a number of cases where people are acting on their values more proactively. Students can probably think of many examples of people whose values influence their lives in a major way.

The Activity sheet, 'My personal values', gives students the opportunity to think about what is really important to them. The writing frame is deliberately open-ended to allow for the widest possible response.

Plenary

Students should look back at their list of how we care for valuable things. How does this relate to how we care for our values? Some will relate directly, the Bible, for example, and other religious books could be said to be places where the teachings of faith are kept safe. Others don't apply at all, for example, most people want to share their values with as many other people as possible. How do we keep our values safe?

Diversity and values

Activity sheet – Personal values

What do you value?

☞ 1 Your house is about to be destroyed. You have ten minutes to collect together the things you value most. Write down the things you would take.

_____   _____

_____   _____

_____   _____

_____   _____

☞ 2 We can't always pick up the things we value the most. Look at the words below. They are all things which might be said to be valuable. Add two ideas of your own in the spaces at the bottom. Now design a symbol for each one. The first one has been done for you.

LOVE	FAMILY	TRUST
HONESTY	FRIENDSHIP	FAIRNESS
RESPECT	_____	_____

Values in everyday life

Diversity and values

Activity sheet – Personal values

What would you do?

☞ 1 Look at the situations on the Resource sheet, 'Values in everyday life'. The first cartoon is about honesty. What values are the other three cartoons about? (**Hint:** look back at the list of values on the Activity sheet, 'What do you value?'.) Write the values as titles on each of the lines below and then write down what you would do in each situation on the lines underneath the pictures.

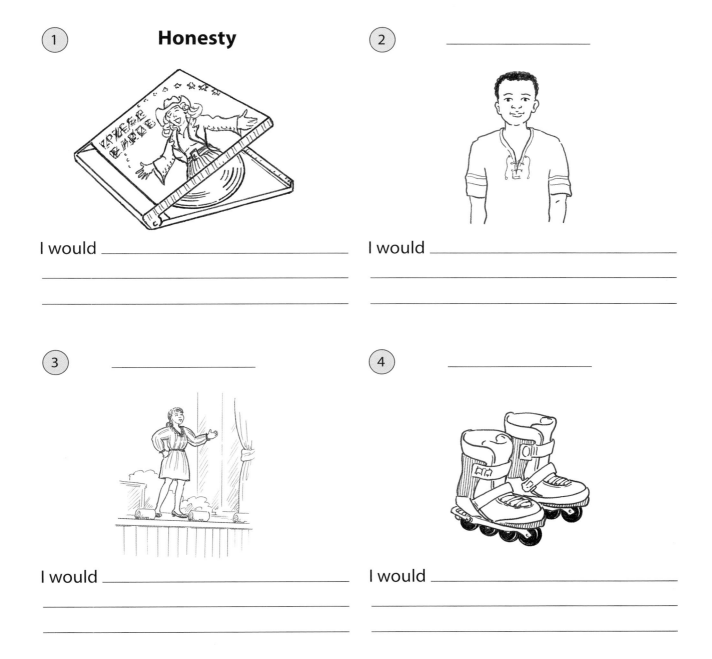

① **Honesty**

I would _____

_____

_____

② _____

I would _____

_____

_____

③ _____

I would _____

_____

_____

④ _____

I would _____

_____

_____

☞ 2 Show what you have written to a partner. Ask them what your comments say about your own personal values.

Values in action

Our values show every day in the small things we do, but some people have such strong values that they feel they have to act on them in a bigger way. Read the comments below.

I can't bare cruelty to animals. I hold jumble sales to raise money for the RSPCA, I write letters to supermarkets encouraging them to stock meat from farms where the animals are well treated and I have been on a number of demonstrations campaigning for animal rights.

I am a Jehovah's Witness. I go with my dad from door to door offering to tell people about Jesus. I know some people find it annoying, but I believe we should share the teaching of Jesus. It wouldn't be right to keep the good news to ourselves.

There are hundreds of people in prisons all over the world just for speaking out against cruel or unfair governments. I am a member of Amnesty International. We write letters to these prisoners and we campaign for their release.

I gave up my car because global warming is a real threat. I cycle most places now and use public transport for long distances.

☞ Imagine you are one of the people above. Write a letter to a friend. Your letter should:

- describe the cause you support and what you do for it
- explain why you do it
- try to persuade them to help you.

Activity sheet – Personal values

My personal values

- Think about the things that matter to you most.
- Think about the things you believe in.
- Think about what you believe is right and wrong.

☞ 1 Now complete the sentences below. There are no 'right' answers.

What matters to me most in the world is _____

_____

The world would be a better place if _____

_____

I would never _____

_____

I always try to _____

_____

Everyone should _____

_____

If I had to leave money to one charity I would choose _____

_____

I believe _____

_____

People would be happier if _____

_____

Everyone is responsible for _____

_____

This planet is _____

_____

☞ 2 Design a poster which shows your personal values. You could include some of the statements you have written above and could also include things you believe and things that matter to you.

Teacher's notes

Family values

Objectives

- To consider how families differ in their habits
- Think about whether or not family values have changed over the years
- To find ways of resolving conflicts within families
- To consider which values they would want to pass on to their own families

Prior knowledge

Students need to understand the meaning of the word 'values'. Students should have sufficient understanding of the word 'values' if they have worked through the section 'Personal values'.

Links to the PSHE: Personal Well-being KS3 Programme of Study for England

1.1   Personal identities
1.5   Diversity

Links to the Draft Curriculum for Excellence for Scotland

Health and Well-being: Relationships
Social Studies: People, past events and societies

Links to the Personal and Social Education Framework for Wales

Community aspect
Social aspect

Links to the Learning for Life and Work: Local and Global Citizenship requirements for Northern Ireland

Diversity and inclusion

Background

All societies throughout history have included family groups and family values are often remarkably similar across different cultures and traditions. Most families recognise the ideals of nurturing, teaching, loving and supporting. In this respect, humans are quite different from some members of the animal kingdom, many of whom never meet their parents. Families, of course, can also be breeding grounds for abuse.

Starter activity

Ask students what they like doing best with their families. Is there anything special about time spent together as a family?

Resource sheets and Activity sheets

Students should read Brendan's comments on the Resource sheet, 'Family differences', and in groups, talk about how their own families are different or the same as Adam and Brendan's. They can then write their rules for KidSwap individually. Some children may feel they live in two families and you should let them choose which family they write rules for.

The Activity sheet, 'Have things changed?', looks at the question of whether or not traditional families are in decline. Ideally, students should take their six questions home and ask their parents, grandparents or other older relatives to answer them. They could then report back with their findings.

Students should complete the Activity sheet, 'Family clashes', in small groups. Most solutions probably include the advice to talk to their parents. This could probably form the basis of the golden rule. You could ask students how many of them do talk through problems at home. Sometimes it can be difficult to start a conversation when there is a clash. You could role play possible opening lines that students could use.

The Resource sheet, 'Rejecting family values', looks at more profound reasons for disagreements within families. You could read through the comments with the class and talk about what happens when families cannot resolve issues.

Students could then complete the certificate on the Activity sheet, 'Pass it on', individually. The sentence starters are very open ended and you may want to discuss possible ideas as a class before students write their certificates.

Plenary

As a class, write a family values alphabet, listing the values students think families should promote. For example, A is for accepting, B is for 'being there', C is for caring, and so on.

Family differences

Brendan stayed with his best friend Adam while his parents were away. Read his comments.

I used to think all families were the same, but when I stayed with my friend Adam for a week, I realised different families do things differently. At his house, we all sat down to eat the evening meal at a table together. In my house we eat at different times and mostly in front of the telly. At Adam's everyone had to help with the housework on Saturday morning. At home, I have to wash-up and keep my bedroom tidy but mum and dad do the rest. Adam's family all watch the TV together, but my brother and I have TVs in our bedrooms and we usually spend the evenings up there. At home, I'm not allowed to tease my little brother, but Adam's mum didn't say anything when he was teasing his sister even when she got annoyed. Everyone talked more at Adam's and they had music on all the time. It was really noisy and I felt like I had no privacy. Everything was different. Not worse. Just different.

In the TV programme *WifeSwap* two wives swap places. They each leave instructions explaining how things are done in their house.

☞ Imagine you were taking place in a TV programme called *KidSwap*. Write instructions for someone your age explaining how things are done in your home. Write your instructions on a separate piece of paper.

Activity sheet – Family values

Have things changed?

Bill is 98. He thinks that families are not as strong as they used to be. Read his comments.

☞ 1 Tick the boxes to show if you think each one still happens 'most of the time', 'sometimes', or 'not very much'.

In Bill's day	These days this happens…		
	Most of the time	Sometimes	Not very much
Children played outside most of the time			
Children were polite to adults			
Families ate together			
The women did most of the housework			
Families went to church together			
If an adult saw a group of children misbehaving they would tell them off			
Children were smacked if they were naughty			
Divorce was unusual			

Ada thinks differently from Bill. Read her comments.

"People go on about families being in danger but I don't believe it. Families are still about love. Strong families help children to grow, learn and be confident. It doesn't matter if you divorce and remarry, as long as your kids still know you love them."

☞ 2 On a separate piece of paper write a list of six questions which you could ask an older person to find out about family life years ago.

Diversity and values

Family clashes

The people below are all having problems because their own values clash with their family's values.

☞ 1 Discuss or write down what you think each person could do to sort out the problem.

My dad doesn't
let me go out with my mates at the weekends. He says
weekends are family time. It's so boring.

My parents
insist I go to Church with them. I don't even
believe in God.

My mum doesn't
like my friend. She says she's rude and has no
table manners. She says I can't invite her round anymore.

When my Gran
comes to visit, my mum makes me put on a dress
and sit and talk to her. She comes every Sunday and stays for an
hour. I hate it.

☞ 2 What one piece of advice would you give to any family having trouble agreeing on something? Write down one golden rule to help families sort out clashes.

My golden rule for sorting out family clashes

Diversity and values

Rejecting family values

As we grow up, we may find that we don't agree with the values our families seem to have. Read the comments below.

My dad only ever cared about money. He worked long hours and was always tired. Mum said we should be grateful because we had expensive toys and good clothes but I would rather have had dad. I don't want to be that sort of dad.

I didn't realise my parents were racist till I left home. They used some awful words and said that Britain was in a mess because of all the people who moved here. When I met my girlfriend, I knew they wouldn't like her just because she was Asian. We don't visit my parents together often.

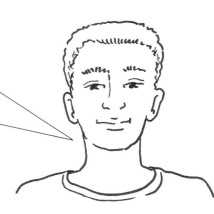

My mum never said she loved me. If I tried to cuddle her she would say 'Don't be so soft.' I know now that she had an awful childhood herself and she probably didn't know how to show me she loved me. It still hurt though.

My parents couldn't see the point in university. They said it would be too expensive and I should get a job. Even now I don't think they're proud of what I've achieved. They both left school at 16 and don't really value education.

Activity sheet – Family values

Pass it on

Read the comments on the Resource sheet, 'Rejecting family values'. It can be sad to find you disagree with your family's values, but growing up is all about making your own choices. As a parent, it will be your job to pass on your values to your own children.

☞ Complete the certificate below as a reminder of the values you might want to pass on.

If I become a parent I will _____
_____
_____

I will also _____
_____
_____

I will teach my children that _____
_____
_____

And I will tell them _____
_____
_____

When we have problems I will _____
_____
_____

I will try never to _____
_____
_____

And I will always do my best to _____
_____
_____

Signed ....

Assessment sheet – Diversity and values

☑ Tick the box to show what applies to you.

	🙂	😐	☹️
I listen to the teacher			
I work well on my own			
I work well with a partner			
I work well in a group			
I can give my own opinion			
I can give a presentation			
I listen to the views of others			
I can look for information			
I can present my work in a way that others can understand			
I can show sympathy and concern for others			
I can understand the good and bad things which people face in their lives			

My targets are:

1 _____

2 _____

3 _____